The Mouse Family

123

by Rosalind Sutton

Illustrated by Pamela Storey

Brimax Books · Newmarket · England

One little mouse is playing ball,
It bounces on the ground;
She throws it up into the air
To catch as it comes down.

Two little mice are on the swings,
Swinging up and down;
They swing so high that they can see
For miles and miles around.

Three little mice have skipping ropes,
They play a counting game;
But one little mouse trips as she jumps
And has to start again.

Four little mice go cycling,
They all enjoy their ride;
They pedal hard up every hill
And race down the other side.

Five little mice play hide and seek,
One counts behind the door;
He turns around and looks about
To find the other four.

Six little mice are on a slide,
All sliding in the sun;
They climb up to the very top
And slip down, one by one.

Seven small mice are dancing,
Together in a ring;
They raise their arms and tap their feet,
Then round and round they swing.

Eight mice are on a picnic,
With cookies and cakes to eat;
They sit down by the river bank
To enjoy their special treat.

Nine little mice are on the ice,
They're skating to and fro;
They like to hold each others' tails
As down the ice they go.

Ten little mice work hard at school,
They have so much to do;
They read and write all morning,
Then paint all afternoon.